This igloo book belongs to:

....

igloobooks

Published in 2022
First published in the UK by Igloo Books Ltd
An imprint of Igloo Books Ltd
Cottage Farm, NN6 0BJ, UK
Owned by Bonnier Books
Sveavägen 56, Stockholm, Sweden
www.igloobooks.com

0122 002
2 4 6 8 10 9 7 5 3
ISBN 978-1-80022-672-2

Illustrated by Nyrryl Cadiz
Written by Everley Hart

Designed by Bethany Dowling
Edited by Claire Mowat

Printed and manufactured in China

ice cream
for
EVERYONE
igloobooks

Butterscotch,
bubblegum,
strawberry delight.
Sweet treats so yummy you must take a bite!

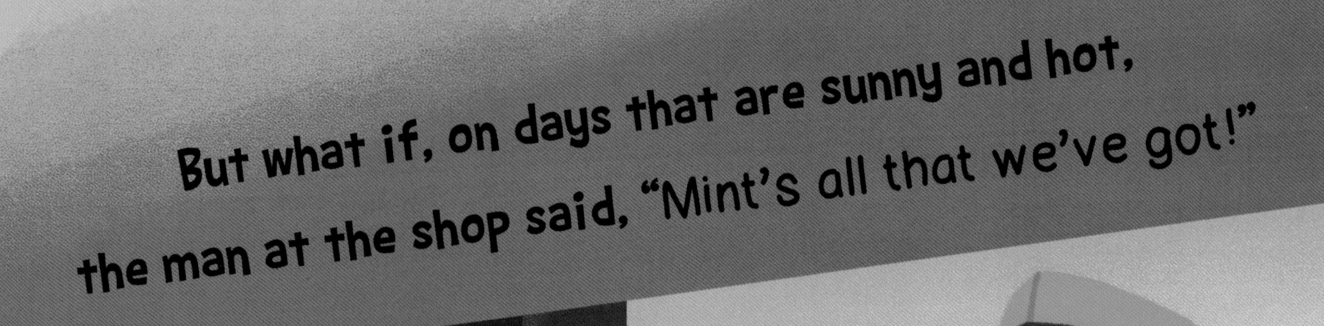

But what if, on days that are sunny and hot,
the man at the shop said, "Mint's all that we've got!"

Mint

Open your dress-up box. Come on, let's play!

Stop, wait a minute. What's different today?

Fairy wings, gone.

Where's your silly clown hair?

"Oh, no! There's only one costume to wear!"

Everyone loves a
fun trip to the zoo.
You find just one animal!
What do you do?

Would you sit patiently
through every show?
Or take the same selfie
ten times in a row?

March to the beat of your musical sound.

The tinkling tune rings
for miles around.

The instruments all make a beautiful song,
but a band with just one makes the whole thing go wrong!

Sway on the monkey bars...
... swing in the sky.
Dig in the sandpit...
... see-saw way up high.

Think of your playground without all those rides.
What if, from now on, it only had... slides?

Look, it's a toy shop!

You **BURST** through the door!

There used to be all sorts of things here before.

Each shelf looks the same as you walk up and down.

"Why is this all that they sell here?" you frown.

Spotty ones chase...

... while the fluffy ones snooze.

Bouncy ones, **licky** ones, how do we choose?

What if we couldn't and, right from the start,
they all looked the same, nothing set them apart?

Get out your crayons,
your paints and
chalks, too.

Let's make a picture.
But wait, there's just...

blue?

You need more than blue for a great work of art.

The world's full of colour.
Blue's only the start!

... oh how **drab!**

That would be such a **bore!**

If life was like that then...

... I'D DOZE OFF AND SNORE.

Let's come together. It's time for some fun!

Meet us, there'll be...

... ICE CREAM FOR EVERYONE!

Many more flavours for all to enjoy.
All different kinds of girls.
All different boys.

So much to do and see. Don't you agree?

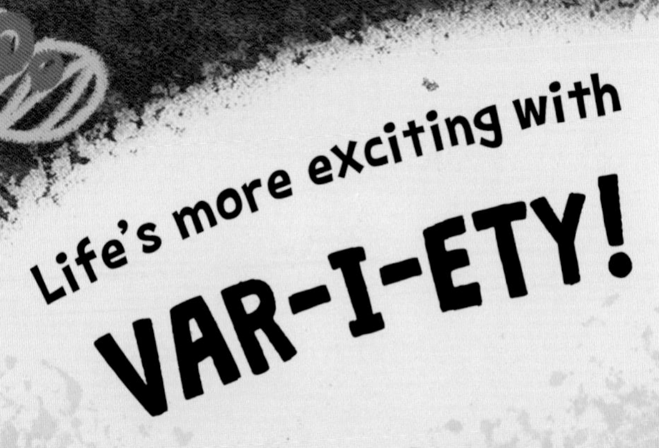